STUDENT VERSION

Intermediate Algebra
SECOND EDITION
A Graphing Approach

K. Elayn Martin-Gay • Margaret Greene

Prentice
Hall

Upper Saddle River, NJ 07458

Designer: Dave Roh
Executive Editor: Karin E. Wagner
Media Project Manager: Audra Walsh
Senior Product Manager: Barbara Wetherington
Product Manager: Ian Seekell
Assistant Managing Editor, Math Media Production: John Matthews
Production Editor: Donna Crilly
Supplement Cover Management/Design: PM Workshop Inc.
Content Manager: Phil Lanza
Media Buyer: Thomas Mangan

© 2001 by Prentice-Hall, Inc.
Upper Saddle River, NJ 07458

Printed in the United States of America

10 9 8 7 6 5 4 3 2 1

ISBN   0-13-018587-6

Prentice-Hall International (UK) Limited, London
Prentice-Hall of Australia Pty. Limited, Sydney
Prentice-Hall Canada, Inc., Toronto
Prentice-Hall Hispanoamericana, S.A., Mexico City
Prentice-Hall of India Private Limited, New Delhi
Pearson Education Asia Pte. Ltd., Singapore
Prentice-Hall of Japan, Inc., Tokyo
Editora Prentice-Hall do Brazil, Ltda., Rio de Janeiro

Contents

Welcome to MathPro5!

MathPro5 is a Web-based version of your math textbook and is organized in a similar format. For each objective in your text, MathPro5 offers a corresponding set of warm-up and exercise problems. Some objectives also provide an instructional video.

MathPro5 generates a set of problems to solve for each learning objective. Whereas textbooks can only show a few examples in each section, MathPro5 allows students to:

- View multiple examples of similar problems
- View the complete solution to any problem
- Work through an interactive step by step process to solve a problem
- Score their work and view an individual Gradebook
- Generate new sets of problems for further practice
- Send messages to their instructors
- Take and score tests.

For the most recent information on MathPro5, please visit www.mathpro5.com/support

MathPro5 System Requirements

WINDOWS REQUIREMENTS
- Pentium 200-MHz processor-based computer or better
- Windows 95, 98, ME, NT 4.0 or 2000
- 32 MB of available RAM (64 MB recommended, required for Windows 2000)
- VGA display, thousands of colors or more (800x600 resolution or higher required)
- 4x Speed or faster CD ROM drive if you want to view the videos from the CD
- Sound card
- Internet Explorer 5.x or higher
- Ability to connect to the Internet, any 56Kbps or better modem
- QuickTime 5 or higher
- Java 1.3 Plug-in
- TestGen-EQ plug-in

MACINTOSH REQUIREMENTS
- 200-MHz or faster Power Macintosh Computer (PowerPC 604 minimum; PowerPC G3 recommended)
- Mac OS 8.1 or OS 9 (OS 8.6 or OS 9 recommended)
- 40 MB of available RAM with virtual memory on and set to at least 44 MB (64 MB recommended)
- 13-inch or larger color display, thousands of color or more (800x600 resolution or higher required)
- 4x Speed or faster CD-ROM drive if you want to view the videos from the CD
- Ability to connect to the Internet, any 56Kbps or better modem
- Internet Explorer 5.x or higher
- QuickTime 5 or higher
- Mac OS Runtime for Java (MRJ 2.2.4)
- TestGen-EQ Plug-in

Installation Instructions

Students will find the MathPro5 CD-ROM in their MathPro5 Student User's Guides and have the option of installing components from the CD.

CD installation is optional, because videos can be streamed over the Internet and the Java plug-in and TestGen-EQ plug-ins can be downloaded from the Internet. However, streaming videos over the Internet can be a slow process depending on modem speed and can result in less than optimal video quality; therefore CD installation is recommended. Videos will load more quickly and play more smoothly if the student has installed the CD and has the CD in the drive while working within MathPro5. It is also quicker to install the required plug-ins from the CD than to download them from the Internet.

WINDOWS: To install the CD:
1. Insert the CD in the CD-ROM drive.
2. Go to the Start menu and select Run. Type x:setup.exe where x is the letter of your CD-ROM drive.
3. Follow the instructions on screen to complete the installation.

This setup program will check your system for the presence of the necessary software to run MathPro5 (Internet Explorer 5.x or higher, Sun Java Plug-in, QuickTime 5 or higher, and TestGen-EQ plug-in). If any of these components are missing or are not the latest versions, the setup program will offer to install them for you.

MAC: To install the components needed to run MathPro5:
1. Insert the CD in the CD-ROM drive
2. To install Internet Explorer version 5, simply drag the folder named Internet Explorer 5 Folder off the CD to any location on your Macintosh.
3. To install the Java Runtime Environment, double-click on the icon named "Install Java".
4. To install QuickTime 5, double-click on the icon named "Install QuickTime 5".
5. To install the TestGen-EQ plug-in, double-click on the icon named "TestGen-EQ plug-in.

If you need technical support, please call the Prentice Hall Media Support Line:

1-800-677-6337

8:00 A.M.– 5:00 P.M. CST Monday through Friday

or email us at media.support@pearsoned.com.

Student Login

1. Open an Internet Connection and use Internet Explorer as the browser.
2. Type the URL **www.mathpro5.com** into the address line of the browser.
3. Click the "Launch MathPro5" link.
4. If this is the first time you are accessing the MathPro5 Website, click on the "Registration" link.

The Access Code is a six-word code: for example, PEOPLE-ACTION-GEORGE-FORIC-TAPE-PLANT.
Look in the back of your MathPro5 manual to find your Access Code.

5. Follow the instructions on the Access Code screen and on subsequent screens.
6. After you have successfully registered, you will return to the MathPro5 login screen. Enter the Username and Password that you set up during the registration process. Enter the Course ID Code that you received from your instructor. Note: you will have to enter your Username and Password each time you visit MathPro5, but you will only have to enter your Course ID Code the first time you access the MathPro5 site.

The Syllabus Screen

After logging into the program, you will see the Syllabus screen. The Syllabus is set up to correspond to the format of your textbook. Your instructor may customize the Syllabus to rearrange objectives, remove chapters, and add additional Problem Sets and Tests.

The Syllabus screen contains four buttons:

 The Go To button is located at the top of the Syllabus screen. Click this button to return to the last Objective or Problem Set in which you were working.

 The Gradebook button is located on the side panel of the Syllabus screen. Click this button to open your Gradebook. See the "Gradebook Screen" section of this document for more detail.

 The Messages button is located on the side panel of the Syllabus screen. Click this button to send messages to your instructor and to view messages your instructor has sent to you. See the "Messages Screen" section of this document for more detail.

 The Help button is located on the side panel of the Syllabus screen. Click the Help button to open a general Help menu. Use Help for explanations of button functionality and assistance navigating within the Syllabus.

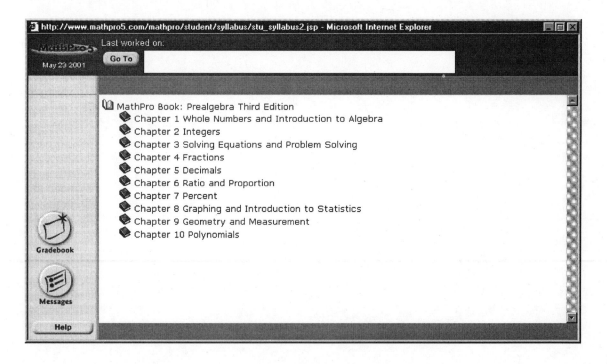

Syllabus Icons

Each Syllabus item is preceded by an icon, which is a symbol designed to provide you with more information about each item. You will see the following icons in the Syllabus:

 The Expanded Heading icon signifies that there are items under this heading in the Syllabus, and those items are displayed. Note: when you have many headings open in your Syllabus at the same time, you may need to use the scroll bar on the right side of the screen to move up and down in your Syllabus.

 The Unexpanded Heading icon signifies that items are available under this heading in the Syllabus, but are not being displayed. Click on an Unexpanded Heading icon to see the items contained under that heading.

The Completed Heading icon signifies that you have completed all the items contained within this heading.

The Item icon represents an Objective item, a Problem Set item at the section or chapter level, or a Test. Click on the icon to open the item.

The Completed Item icon signifies that this item has been completed.

The Instructor Note icon next to a Syllabus item signifies that there is a note from your instructor attached to that particular Syllabus icon. Click on the icon to open the Instructor Note.

Objective Warm-Ups and Exercises

When you click on an Objective in the Syllabus, you go directly to the Warm-Ups screen. Note that the background of the Warm-Ups button is dark blue, indicating that you are currently on the Warm-Ups screen. The button will become light blue when you move to the Exercises or Watch screen. On the Warm-Ups screen, you can work on practice problems that will not be graded. You can click on the Exercises button to open a set of graded problems for the same Objective. The Exercises screen looks identical to the Warm-Ups screen, except that the Exercises screen has a box displaying your score in the blue strip above the answer space. The Warm-Ups screen has no score box since none of the problems are graded. In both the Warm-Ups and Exercises, the problem and instructions appear on the left side of the screen and you enter your answer in the answer space on the right side of the screen. The following buttons are available to you in the Warm-Ups and Exercises:

▦ The Math Tools button is located in the answer space on the right side of the screen. Click this button to open the Tool Palette. You can use the Tool Palette to help you enter appropriate math
symbols in the answer space. See the "Math Tools" section of this document for more information on the various math tools available to you.

Check Answer. The Check Answer button is located in the answer space on the right side of the screen. Once you have entered your answer into the answer space, click this
button or use the Enter key on your keyboard to see if you answered correctly.

▶ The Forward Arrow button is located in the blue strip above the math problem. Click this button to move to the next math problem in the set. Once you have finished the last problem in a set, the
Forward Arrow button will disappear and only the Back Arrow button will be available to you.

◀ The Back Arrow button is located in the blue strip above the math problem. Click this button to go back to a previous problem in the set.

Return to Syllabus

The Return to Syllabus button is located on the side panel of the screen. Click this button to return to the Syllabus at any time. If you then exit the MathPro5 program, the Syllabus will keep track of where you were working within the program and you can use the Go To button to return to that Objective.

Glossary

The Glossary button is located on the side panel of the screen. Click this button to open a glossary of math terms.

Help The Help button is located on the side panel of the screen. Click this button to open a general Help menu. Use Help for explanations of button functionality and
assistance with navigation. Also provided in Help is a link to a News and Updates page were you can get the latest information about MathPro5.

Several buttons appear at the bottom of the Warm-Ups and Exercises screens to help you work through the problems: View Example, Step-by-Step, View Solution, Redo Problem, and New Set. These buttons are described in detail in the pages that follow. Your instructor can decide which of these support buttons are available to you. If one or more of the buttons do not appear on your Warm-Ups or Exercises screens, this is due to the way your instructor set up the course.

View Example

View Example Click on the View Example button to generate an example problem similar to the one on which you are currently working. The example problem will appear below the original problem on the left side of the screen. The steps to solve the problem and the final solution to the example problem are given. When you have viewed and understood the example problem, you can then solve the original problem and enter an answer in the answer space on the right side of the screen.

Welcome to MathPro 5 - Microsoft Internet Explorer

MathPro 5
May 18 2001

3.1.A Use properties of numbers to combine like terms.

Watch   Warm-Ups   Exercises

Return to Syllabus

▶ Problem 1 of 10 ■

View Example

$3z + 1 - 2$

Like terms are terms that have the same variables and powers of those variables, but may have different numerical coefficients. Constants, which have no variables at all, are also like terms.
In the given expression 1 and -2 are like terms. They are both constants.
Combine the like terms.

$$3z + 1 - 2 = 3z + (1 - 2) = 3z - 1$$

Glossary

Help

1. **Enter your answer.**

2. [Click here to check answer.]

View Example   Step-by-Step   View Solution   Redo Problem   New Set

8

Step-by-Step

Step-by-Step Click on the Step-by-Step button to receive guidance for each step of solving a problem. The first step appears on the left side of the screen under the original problem. Enter an answer to the first step on the right side of the screen in the answer space and click the button to check your answer. Continue entering answers for each step of the process and clicking the Check Answer button to see if your answer is correct. When you have finished solving the problem, click on the End Step-by-Step button to return to the main problem set. You may use Step-by-Step support only once per problem, but you can use it for all the problems in the set if you wish. **If you use the Step-by-Step feature in the Exercises, you will not receive credit for the problem.**

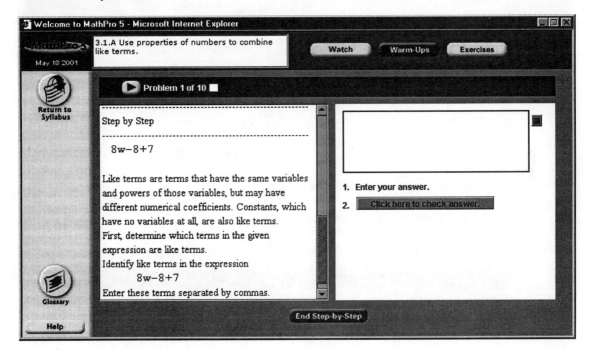

View Solution

View Solution Click the View Solution button to see the solution to the problem on which you are currently working. The solution appears on the left side of the screen under the original problem. Once you have clicked on View Solution, you will not be able to enter an answer for that problem in the answer space on the right side of the screen. **If you use the View Solution button in the Exercises, you will not receive credit for that problem.**

Welcome to MathPro 5 - Microsoft Internet Explorer

MathPro 5
May 18 2001

3.1.A Use properties of numbers to combine like terms.

Watch   Warm-Ups   Exercises

▶ Problem 1 of 10 ■

Return to Syllabus

View Solution

$8w - 8 + 7$

Like terms are terms that have the same variables and powers of those variables, but may have different numerical coefficients. Constants, which have no variables at all, are also like terms.
In the given expression -8 and 7 are like terms. They are both constants.
Combine the like terms.

$$8w - 8 + 7 = 8w + (-8 + 7) = 8w - 1$$

1. **Enter your answer.**

2.

Glossary

Help

View Example   Step-by-Step   View Solution   Redo Problem   New Set

Redo Problem

Redo Problem Click on the Redo Problem button if you get the original problem incorrect and would like to try another problem of the same type. Another similar problem will be generated below your original problem. If you get the problem incorrect again, you can continue to press Redo until you understand the problem type and are able to get a problem correct. If you are working in the Exercises, each time you use the Redo button another problem will be added to the overall set. The system tracks both your original incorrect problem and the new problem. You will not see the number of problems change in the blue bar, but your score will reflect the total number of problems you did, including the Redo problems. For example, if you have a set of five problems and you get one wrong, you will receive a score of 80%. If you use the Redo button to generate another problem for the problem you got wrong and you get the Redo problem correct, you will now have a total of six problems with one incorrect problem. Your total score would then rise to 83%.

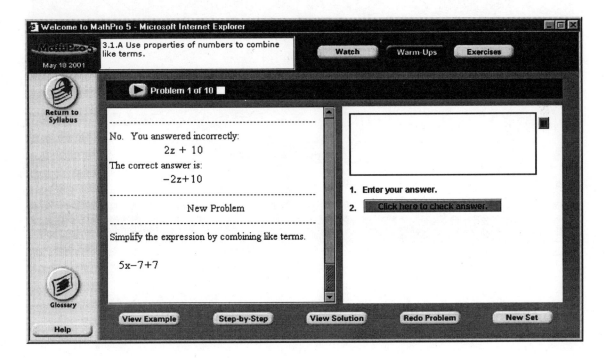

New Set

New Set   Click on the New Set button to generate an entirely new set of Warm-Up or Exercise problems. Your instructor has the ability to limit the number of times the New Set button can be used within the Warm-Ups and Exercises. Your Gradebook displays the number of times you choose to use the New Set button on an Exercise screen for each Objective. When the new set of problems has been generated, a message will appear, and you can click OK to accept the new set of problems.

Math Tools

Open the Tool Palette by clicking on the Math Tools button in the answer space. Click the x in the top right corner of the Tool Palette to close it. This Tool Palette can be accessed on both the Warm-Ups screen and the Exercises screen, and in any additional problem sets that your instructor has added to your Syllabus. With your mouse, move your cursor over each item in the Tool Palette to see a pop-up description of that item. Put your cursor in the answer space and then select the appropriate button in the Tool Palette to insert that symbol into the answer space. Each button is described below.

Note: for access to a calculator, use the calculator in the system resources for your computer. For PC users, click on the Start button on your taskbar, select Programs, then select Accessories. Chose Calculator from the drop-down list. For Mac users, click on the Apple icon on the desktop and select Calculator from the drop-down list.

Inserts a plus or positive sign at the position of the cursor. You can also use the + key on your keyboard.

Inserts a minus or negative sign at the position of the cursor. You can also use the − key on your keyboard.

Inserts a multiplication sign at the position of the cursor. You can also use Ctrl+8 on your keyboard. (Note that this is not a decimal point. Use the period on your keyboard as a decimal point.)

Inserts a division sign at the position of the cursor.

Inserts a plus/minus sign at the position of the cursor. You can also use Ctrl+= on your keyboard.

Inserts an equal to symbol at the position of the cursor. You can also use the = sign on your keyboard.

Inserts a not equal to symbol at the position of the cursor. You can also use Ctrl+3 on your keyboard.

Inserts an approximately equal to symbol at the position of the cursor.

Inserts an absolute value symbol. Highlight the value in the answer space and click the absolute value button to put absolute value symbols around that value. Or click the absolute value button first and then click on the absolute value symbol in the answer space and type in a value. You can also use Ctrl+a on your keyboard.

Click the Exponent button to enter an exponent. You can also use Ctrl+6 on your keyboard or the ^.

- For example, to enter x^2, type x and click the Exponent button. This gives you the expression $x^{\square}$. Then type a 2 in the exponent box.
- If you have already typed an expression and want to put it in an exponent, highlight the expression and click the Exponent button. For example, if you typed 5 and you want 5 to be an exponent, highlight 5 and click the Exponent button. This will give you the expression x^5. You can click in the box or click the left arrow key on your keyboard to enter a base.
- When you are done typing an exponent on a base, remember to click your cursor to the right of the exponential expression in order to leave the superscript mode. You can also use the right arrow button on your keyboard.

Click the Subscript button to enter a subscript value. You can also use Ctrl+__ on your keyboard.

- For example, to enter x_1, type x and click the Subscript button. This will give you $x_{\square}$. Then type a 1 in the subscript box.
- If you have already typed an expression and want to put it in a subscript, highlight the expression and click the Subscript button. For example, if you typed $6x$ and you want $6x$ to be subscript, highlight $6x$ and click the Subscript button. This will give you the expression x_{6x}. You can click in the box or hit the left arrow key on your keyboard to enter a base.
- When you are done typing a subscript on a base, remember to click your cursor to the right of the expression to leave the subscript mode. You can also use the right arrow key on your keyboard.

Click the Square Root button to enter a square root. You can also use Ctrl+s on your keyboard.

- For example, to enter $\sqrt{x+9}$, click the Square Root button and type x + 9 in the radicand box.

 Click the nth Root button to enter any root. You can also use Ctrl+r on your keyboard.

- For example, to enter $\sqrt[4]{16}$, click the nth Root button. The cursor will be in the box under the radical. Type 16. Then click in the box outside the radical or press the left arrow key and type 4.
- If you have already typed an expression, highlight the expression and click the nth Root button. This will put the expression under the radical and put the cursor in the small box outside the radical.

Click the Fraction/Rational Expression button to enter a rational expression. You can also use Ctrl+/ on your keyboard.

- For example, to enter the fraction $\frac{2}{3}$, click the Fraction button and type 2 in the numerator. Then click with your cursor in the box for the denominator or click on the right arrow key on your keyboard and type 3.

 Inserts a less than symbol at the position of the cursor. You can also use < on your keyboard.

 Inserts a less than or equal to symbol at the position of the cursor. You can also use Ctrl+, on your keyboard.

 Inserts a greater than symbol at the position of the cursor. You can also use > on your keyboard.

 Inserts a greater than or equal to symbol at the position of the cursor. You can use Ctrl+. on your keyboard.

 Clears all values from the answer box.

 Inserts a set union symbol at the position of the cursor. You can also use Ctrl+9 on your keyboard.

 Inserts a set intersection symbol at the position of the cursor. You can also use Ctrl+0 on your keyboard.

 Inserts a member of set symbol at the position of the cursor.

Inserts a not member of set symbol at the position of the cursor.

Inserts a constant *e* symbol at the position of the cursor. You can also use Ctrl+e on your keyboard.

Inserts a constant *i* symbol at the position of the cursor. You can also use Ctrl+i on your keyboard.

Inserts a Pi symbol at the position of the cursor. You can also use Ctrl+p on your keyboard.

Inserts an infinity symbol at the position of the cursor.

You can use certain keyboard shortcuts to move around within the answer box in addition to using the arrows and your mouse:

Home key: Moves cursor to beginning of expression in answer space.

End key: Moves cursor to end of expression in answer space.

Shift/Home: Highlights all items to the left of the cursor.

Shift/End: Highlights all items to the right of the cursor.

Objective Watch Screen

Watch   Click on the Watch button within an Objective to open a video of a problem being worked related to the current Objective. Each video is approximately one minute long.

A dialog box will open asking if you would like to run the videos from the CD or stream them over the Internet. If you would like to run the videos from the CD-ROM (recommended for better performance and quality), click the "Run videos from CD" button. This setting will remain in effect until you exit your browser. The next time you want to see a video, you will need to reset your preference.

If you don't have the CD-ROM or access to the CD-ROM drive, click the "Run videos from Internet" button. If there is heavy Internet traffic or if you have a slow modem, this streaming process may be slow and the picture and sound may be interrupted from time to time.

If you did not install the CD-ROM and you do not have QuickTime 5 or later on your computer, the first time you attempt to watch a video you will be directed to download QuickTime from the Internet.

Not all objectives have videos associated with them. The Watch button will be grayed for any Objective that doesn't have a video associated with it.

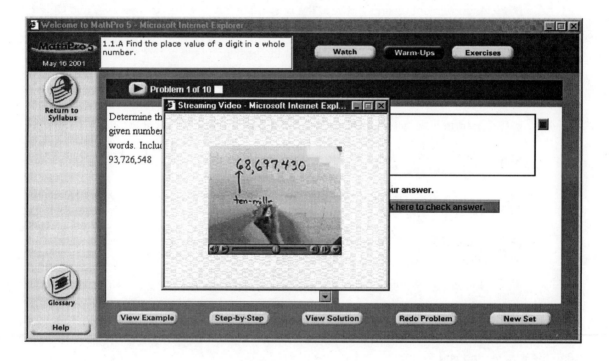

The following buttons are available on the videos:

 Click the Volume button to turn the volume up or down.

Click the Pause button to pause the video. You can pause the video for as long as you choose.

When you have paused the video, the Pause button becomes a Play button. Click the Play button to restart the video. If you are watching the videos streamed from the Internet, there may be a delay as the video loads again after each pause.

 Click on the Scroll bar and drag it to the right or left to move to another place in the video.

Click the Rewind button to move the video back a frame. Hold down the Rewind button to rewind further in the video or use the Scroll bar to move back.

Click the Forward button to move the video forward a frame. Hold down the Forward button to move further forward in the video or use the Scroll bar to move forward.

Click the down-pointing Arrow button to see which version of QuickTime is installed on your computer or to modify your plug-in settings.

Click the Close button in the upper right corner of the video to close the video and return to the Objective screen.

Gradebook Screen

Enter the Gradebook by clicking on the Gradebook button on the Syllabus screen. There are three possible ways the Gradebook button can look. Each one reflects a slightly different set of circumstances:

Gradebook

When you first login to MathPro5, you will see this icon for the Gradebook. This means that there is no data in your Gradebook to show you. You will also see this icon while a report is being generated, for example when you have pressed the refresh button. Your Gradebook will be automatically updated once a day to reflect any new work you did that day.

Gradebook

This icon will be displayed when you have a new Gradebook report that you have not yet viewed. Click the icon to see the new report.

Gradebook

The checkmark in the Gradebook button indicated that you have seen the current data that is in the Gradebook report.

Note that your teacher has access to the same Gradebook information that you see when you view your Gradebook. When your Gradebook is open, you may need to scroll down to see all the items. Your Gradebook report includes your test scores as well as the following information for each Objective Exercise problem set:

- **Time** spent in each item
- **Last Date** the item was opened
- Total **Score** for the item
- Number of problem **Sets** generated
- Number of problems **Correct**
- Number of problems **Incorrect**
- Number of times you accessed **Step-by-Step** (**SBS**) support
- Number of times you accessed **View Solution** support.

There are four buttons on the Gradebook screen:

Return to Syllabus

Click on the Return to Syllabus button to return to the Syllabus at any time.

Help   Click on the Help button for explanation of the terminology used in the Gradebook.

Refresh   Click on the Refresh button to see the most updated version of your Gradebook. Your Gradebook report is automatically generated once a day, but you can use the Refresh button if you need to see grades for work you have just completed that day. Refreshing a Gradebook report can take some time, but you can do other tasks within the program while waiting for the new report to be generated. After pressing Refresh, you will be taken back to the Syllabus screen, letting the report generate while you work on something else within MathPro5.

Export Data   Click the Export Data button to export grades from the Gradebook to the hard drive or the floppy disk of your computer. Once report has been exported, you can print your grades.

Messages Screen

From the Syllabus Screen, you can use the Messages button to go to your Messages Screen. From the Messages Screen, you can send messages to your instructor and view messages your instructor has sent to you. There are three buttons on the side panel of your Messages Screen:

Click the Return to Syllabus button to return to the Syllabus Screen.

Click the Create Messages button to write messages to your instructor. See the "Creating Messages" section of this document for more detail.

Click the Help button to open a general Help menu. Use Help for explanations of button functionality and assistance with navigation.

There are three main buttons at the bottom of your Messages box:

Click on the circle beside the message you want to view and click the Open button. The message will open in a separate window. (Note: only your instructor can send you messages, and you can only send messages to your instructor, not to other students in the class.) Type your response to the instructor's message in the Response box and click Send to send the message back to the instructor. You can also click Clear to clear your reply and start again, Cancel or the x button to close the message window, or Print to print a screen capture of the message.

Select a message and click the Archive button to save the message to the server in a separate folder. You can access your Archived messages at any time by clicking on the Archived link.

Select a message and click the Delete button to erase any messages you do not want to save. You will always get a warning message asking if you are sure you want to delete the message. Choose OK to delete the message or Cancel to save it.

Your messages can be filtered by Received, Sent, and Archived. Click on Received to see all the messages that have been sent to you by your instructor. Click on Sent to display the messages you have sent to your instructor. Click on Archived to see any messages that you previously saved through the Archive button.

Received messages can be further sorted by Read, From, and Date.
- Click on the Read link and then use the up or down arrows to sort with unread messages at the top of the list or at the bottom of the list. An unread message has an empty box beside it, while a previously read message has an X in the box.
- Click on the From link and use the up or down arrows to sort your messages alphabetically according to who sent them. This feature may be useful if you are enrolled in more than one course and have more than one instructor.
- Click on the Date link and use the up or down arrows to sort with the most recent messages at the top or bottom of the list (descending or ascending order based on date message arrived).

Sent messages can be filtered further by Read, To, and Date.
- Click on the Read link and use the up and down arrows to sort with unread messages at the top or bottom of the list.
- Click on the To link and use the up and down arrows to sort your messages alphabetically by instructor name.
- Click on the Date link and use the up or down arrows to sort with the most recent messages at the top or bottom of the list (descending or ascending order based on date message arrived).

Archived messages can be sorted by Type, To, and Date.
- Click on the Type link to sort your messages according to whether they are Sent or Received messages.
- Click on the To link and use the up and down arrows to sort any Sent messages alphabetically by instructor.
- Click on the Date link and use the up or down arrows to sort with the most recent messages at the top or bottom of the list (descending or ascending order based on date message arrived).

Creating Messages

Create Messages

Use the Create Messages button on the side panel of the Messages Screen to write messages to your instructor. This feature is a helpful way to communicate with your instructor if you are having difficulty with an Objective or have questions about due dates or grades. Clicking on the Create Messages button opens a separate window for your message. Type a short heading to describe your message in the Subject box and type the full message in the Message box. Click **Send** to send this message to your instructor. The message window will close automatically when you have sent the message. Click **Clear** to clear all your text from the Subject box and the Message box so that you can start again. Click **Cancel** or the x button at the top right corner of the window to close the message window. Click **Print** to print the message.

New Message - Microsoft Internet Explorer

To: Anthony Beck

Subject:

Math help needed

Message:

```
I need help understanding the Exercise
problems.
```

[Send]   [Clear]   [Cancel]   [Print]

Taking TestGen-EQ Tests

To take a test, simply open the test from your syllabus. If you have not installed the CD-ROM that came with your MathPro5 manual, you will be directed to download the TestGen-EQ plug-in from the Internet so you can access your tests. Before opening a test, be sure you are ready to take the test because you cannot cancel out of the test once you have opened it. Opening a test from the Syllabus takes you directly to the first question in the test. Use your mouse to click on the circle beside the correct answer choice for each problem. If you change your mind, you can click on a different answer choice. The letter you have chosen as the correct answer will appear filled-in. Use the scroll bar on the right side of the test question if you need to scroll down to see the entire question.

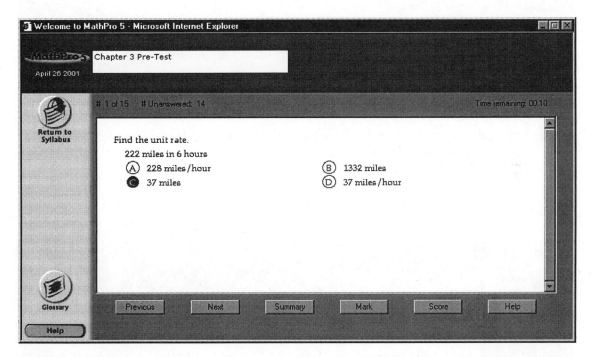

In the top left corner over the test question, you can see the number of the test question you are currently viewing, the total number of questions in the test, and how many unanswered questions remain. The top right corner over the test question displays how much time you have to take the test and counts down the time for you. Your instructor determines whether the test will be a timed or untimed test. If the test is timed, the instructor can set up a pop-up warning message that opens once during the test to tell you how much time you have left. The instructor determines the time at which this warning will appear. Click OK to close the warning message and return to the test. When your time is up, your test will automatically be scored whether or not you have finished the test.

There are several buttons available on the Test screen. The three side panel buttons are the same buttons that are available on the Warm-Ups and Exercises screens.

Click this button to return to the Syllabus. If you have not completed your test, you will receive a warning and you can choose either to complete the test or to return to the Syllabus without completing the test. If you choose to return to the Syllabus without completing your test, the test will still be scored and you will not be able to retake the test.

Click this button to open a glossary of math terms.

Click this button to open a general Help menu. Use Help for explanation of button functionality and assistance navigating within MathPro5.

In addition to the side panel buttons, there are six buttons at the bottom of the Test screen. The buttons are described in detail on the following pages.

Previous   Click on the Previous button to move back to a previous test question. This button is useful if you want to review your answers or change an answer for a problem you have already completed.

Next   Click the Next button to move forward to the next problem in the test.

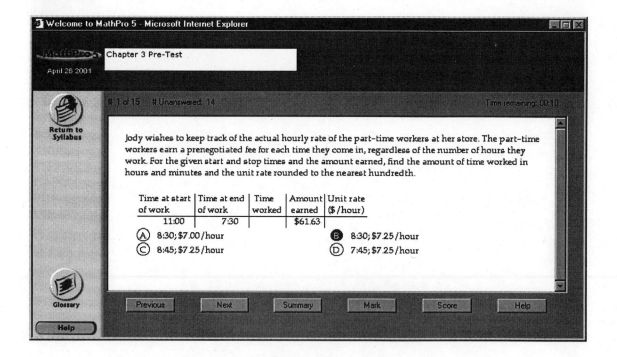

Click the Summary button at any time while you are taking the test. The Summary screen lists all the questions on the test and you can see the letter answer you chose for each question. The questions you have not answered yet will be blank. The test question you are currently on is highlighted. If you have skipped a question and marked it, there will be an asterisk next to the question number on the Summary screen to remind you to return to it. If you view the Summary after scoring your test, an X beside the letter choice indicates an incorrect answer. From the Summary screen, click on any question to go directly to that question in the test, or use the Back button to return to the problem you are currently solving. In the example shown here, the student has completed test questions 1, 2, and 4 and is currently on question 4 in the test. She has skipped question 3 in the test and marked it so she will remember to return to it before scoring her test.

Welcome to MathPro 5 - Microsoft Internet Explorer

MathPro 5
April 26 2001

Chapter 3 Pre-Test

Return to Syllabus

Summary

1 B	4 C	7	10	13	
2 B	5	8	11	14	
3 *	6	9	12	15	

Click a question number to go to that question.
Asterisks (*) indicate 'marked' questions.
An (x) indicates questions answered incorrectly.

Glossary

Help

Back

Mark Click the Mark button if you are currently viewing a test question that you want to skip. When you have finished the other questions in the test, you can click the Summary button to quickly see which questions you have marked. The marked questions will have asterisks next to them on the Summary screen. From the Summary screen, click on the marked question to return directly to that question in the test. Or you can return to your marked questions by clicking on the Previous button and moving back through the test questions one by one.

Click on the Help button for descriptions of button functionality on the Test screen. Click the Back button to return to the test.

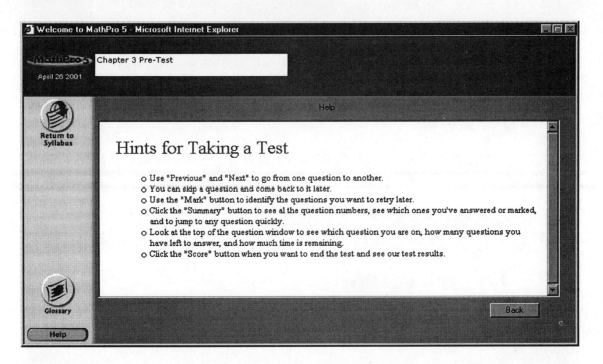

Click on the Score button when you have finished answering all the questions in the test. The # Unanswered questions above your test should show 0 before you click on the Score button. If you have forgotten to answer a question, you will receive the following warning when you click on the Score button:

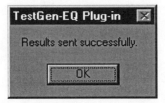

Press Yes if you want to score the test even though it is not finished. Click No if you want to return to the test to complete the unanswered questions. Use the Summary button to see which questions you have not answered, and select answers for them. Then press Score again when you are ready to score the test.

When your test has been scored, you will see the following message:

Click OK to close the message, and to see a summary of your test scores. The Test Scores screen shows you the number of correct and incorrect problems, the total number of problems in the test, your score, and the amount of time you spent in the test.

```
┌──────────────────────────────────────────────────────────────────────────────┐
│ 🗗 Welcome to MathPro 5 - Microsoft Internet Explorer          _ □ ✕           │
├──────────────────────────────────────────────────────────────────────────────┤
│  MathPro 5  ┌────────────────────────────────────────────┐                    │
│             │ Chapter 3 Pre-Test                          │                    │
│ April 26 2001└────────────────────────────────────────────┘                   │
│                                                                                │
│  ╔═══════╗                        Test Scores                                  │
│  ║       ║   ┌──────────────────────────────────────────────────────────┐ ▲   │
│  ╚═══════╝   │                                                           │     │
│  Return to   │                                                           │     │
│  Syllabus    │         Correct:       3                                  │     │
│              │         Incorrect:     12                                 │     │
│              │         Total:         15                                 │     │
│              │         Score:         20%                                │     │
│              │         Time Spent     00:09 min.                         │     │
│              │                                                           │     │
│  ╔═══════╗   │                                                           │     │
│  ║       ║   │   Select "Review" to review the correct answers for the   │     │
│  ╚═══════╝   │   test questions.                                         │     │
│  Glossary    │                                                           │ ▼   │
│              └──────────────────────────────────────────────────────────┘     │
│  ┌────────┐              ┌──────────┐        ┌──────────┐                      │
│  │  Help  │              │  Review  │        │   Done   │                      │
│  └────────┘              └──────────┘        └──────────┘                      │
└──────────────────────────────────────────────────────────────────────────────┘
```

Click the **Done** button on the Test Scores screen if you want to return to the Syllabus. You can return to your test from the Syllabus to review it at any time, but you cannot rescore your test.

Click the **Review** button on the Test Scores screen to go through your test problems one by one. Review allows you to compare your answer to the correct answer for each test question. Your answer choice is the filled-in letter. The correct answer is highlighted in blue. In the upper right corner of the Test Review screen, you can see your percentage score for the test. During the Review process, you can click on the Done button to return to the Syllabus, the Previous button to go back to a previous test question, or the Next button to move to the next test question.

From the Test Review screen, click on **Summary** if you want to see an overview of your answers to all the test questions. The incorrect questions will have an X beside them. Click the Back button to return to reviewing the test questions. Or click on a particular question in the Summary to go directly back to reviewing that question in the test.

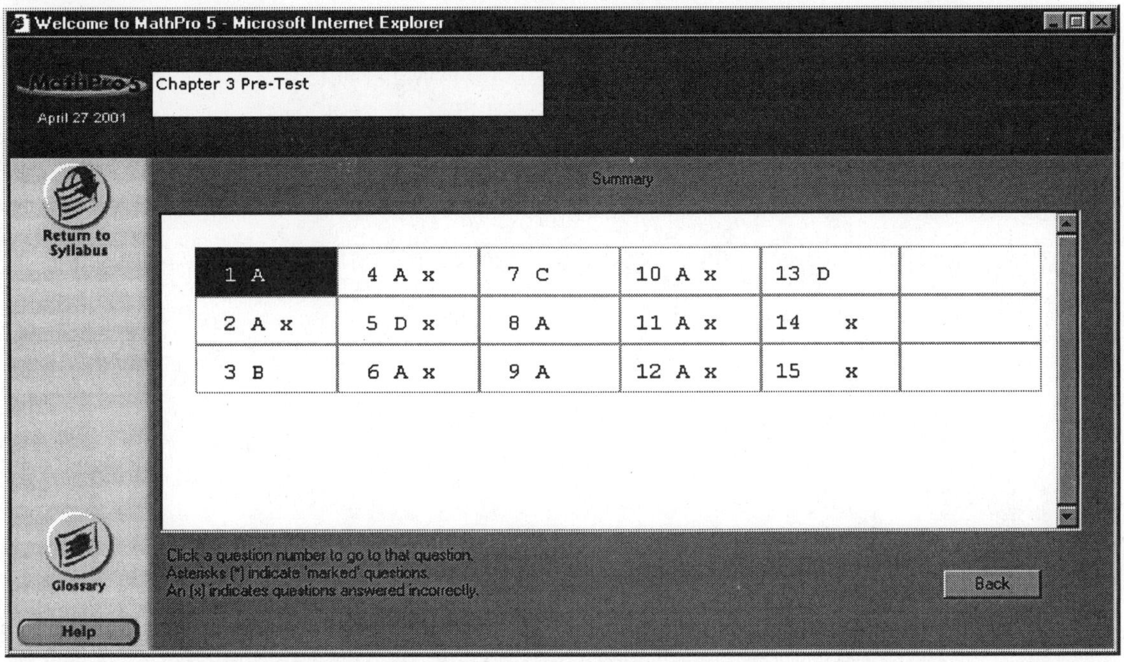

The screenshot shows the MathPro 5 Summary screen with the following content:

- Welcome to MathPro 5 - Microsoft Internet Explorer
- Chapter 3 Pre-Test
- April 27 2001
- Return to Syllabus
- Glossary
- Help
- Summary

1 A	4 A x	7 C	10 A x	13 D	
2 A x	5 D x	8 A	11 A x	14 x	
3 B	6 A x	9 A	12 A x	15 x	

Click a question number to go to that question.
Asterisks (*) indicate 'marked' questions.
An [x] indicates questions answered incorrectly.

Back

29

MathPro Development Team

Design and Management

Designer: Dave Roh
Senior Product Manager: Barbara Wetherington
Product Manager: Ian Seekell
Content Manager: Philip Lanza

Content

Tanya Allain	Jack Janssen
Michael Duguay	Jenn Mangan
Katherine Gregory	Virginia Pyle
Lynne Hozik	

SINGLE PC LICENSE AGREEMENT AND LIMITED WARRANTY

READ THIS LICENSE CAREFULLY BEFORE OPENING THIS PACKAGE. BY OPENING THIS PACKAGE, YOU ARE AGREEING TO THE TERMS AND CONDITIONS OF THIS LICENSE. IF YOU DO NOT AGREE, DO NOT OPEN THE PACKAGE. PROMPTLY RETURN THE UNOPENED PACKAGE AND ALL ACCOMPANYING ITEMS TO THE PLACE YOU OBTAINED THEM. THESE TERMS APPLY TO ALL LICENSED SOFTWARE ON THE DISK EXCEPT THAT THE TERMS FOR USE OF ANY SHAREWARE OR FREEWARE ON THE DISKETTES ARE AS SET FORTH IN THE ELECTRONIC LICENSE LOCATED ON THE DISK:

1. GRANT OF LICENSE and OWNERSHIP: The enclosed MathPro Explorer computer programs and data ("Software") are licensed, not sold, to you by Prentice-Hall, Inc. ("We" or the "Company") and in consideration of your purchase or adoption of the accompanying Company textbooks and/or other materials, and your agreement to these terms. We reserve any rights not granted to you. You own only the disk(s) but we and/or our licensors own the Software itself. This license allows you to use and display your copy of the Software on a single computer (i.e., with a single CPU) at a single location for academic use only, so long as you comply with the terms of this Agreement. You may make one copy for back up, or transfer your copy to another CPU, provided that the Software is usable on only one computer.

2. RESTRICTIONS: You may not transfer or distribute the Software or documentation to anyone else. Except for backup, you may not copy the documentation or the Software. You may not network the Software or otherwise use it on more than one computer or computer terminal at the same time. You may not reverse engineer, disassemble, decompile, modify, adapt, translate, or create derivative works based on the Software or the Documentation. You may be held legally responsible for any copying or copyright infringement which is caused by your failure to abide by the terms of these restrictions.

3. TERMINATION: This license is effective until terminated. This license will terminate automatically without notice from the Company if you fail to comply with any provisions or limitations of this license. Upon termination, you shall destroy the Documentation and all copies of the Software. All provisions of this Agreement as to limitation and disclaimer of warranties, limitation of liability, remedies or damages, and our ownership rights shall survive termination.

4. LIMITED WARRANTY AND DISCLAIMER OF WARRANTY: Company warrants that for a period of 60 days from the date you purchase this SOFTWARE (or purchase or adopt the accompanying textbook), the Software, when properly installed and used in accordance with the Documentation, will operate in substantial conformity with the description of the Software set forth in the Documentation, and that for a period of 30 days the disk(s) on which the Software is delivered shall be free from defects in materials and workmanship under normal use. The Company does not warrant that the Software will meet your requirements or that the operation of the Software will be uninterrupted or error-free. Your only remedy and the Company's only obligation under these limited warranties is, at the Company's option, return of the disk for a refund of any amounts paid for it by you or replacement of the disk. THIS LIMITED WARRANTY IS THE ONLY WARRANTY PROVIDED BY THE COMPANY AND ITS LICENSORS, AND THE COMPANY AND ITS LICENSORS DISCLAIM ALL OTHER WARRANTIES, EXPRESS OR IMPLIED, INCLUDING WITHOUT LIMITATION, THE IMPLIED WARRANTIES OF MERCHANTABILITY AND FITNESS FOR A PARTICULAR PURPOSE. THE COMPANY DOES NOT WARRANT, GUARANTEE OR MAKE ANY REPRESENTATION REGARDING THE ACCURACY, RELIABILITY, CURRENTNESS, USE, OR RESULTS OF USE, OF THE SOFTWARE.

5. LIMITATION OF REMEDIES AND DAMAGES: IN NO EVENT, SHALL THE COMPANY OR ITS EMPLOYEES, AGENTS, LICENSORS, OR CONTRACTORS BE LIABLE FOR ANY INCIDENTAL, INDIRECT, SPECIAL, OR CONSEQUENTIAL DAMAGES ARISING OUT OF OR IN CONNECTION WITH THIS LICENSE OR THE SOFTWARE, INCLUDING FOR LOSS OF USE, LOSS OF DATA, LOSS OF INCOME OR PROFIT, OR OTHER LOSSES, SUSTAINED AS A RESULT OF INJURY TO ANY PERSON, OR LOSS OF OR DAMAGE TO PROPERTY, OR CLAIMS OF THIRD PARTIES, EVEN IF THE COMPANY OR AN AUTHORIZED REPRESENTATIVE OF THE COMPANY HAS BEEN ADVISED OF THE POSSIBILITY OF SUCH DAMAGES. IN NO EVENT SHALL THE LIABILITY OF THE COMPANY FOR DAMAGES WITH RESPECT TO THE SOFTWARE EXCEED THE AMOUNTS ACTUALLY PAID BY YOU, IF ANY, FOR THE SOFTWARE OR THE ACCOMPANYING TEXTBOOK. BECAUSE SOME JURISDICTIONS DO NOT ALLOW THE LIMITATION OF LIABILITY IN CERTAIN CIRCUMSTANCES, THE ABOVE LIMITATIONS MAY NOT ALWAYS APPLY TO YOU.

6. GENERAL: THIS AGREEMENT SHALL BE CONSTRUED IN ACCORDANCE WITH THE LAWS OF THE UNITED STATES OF AMERICA AND THE STATE OF NEW YORK, APPLICABLE TO CONTRACTS MADE IN NEW YORK, AND SHALL BENEFIT THE COMPANY, ITS AFFILIATES AND ASSIGNEES. HIS AGREEMENT IS THE COMPLETE AND EXCLUSIVE STATEMENT OF THE AGREEMENT BETWEEN YOU AND THE COMPANY AND SUPERSEDES ALL PROPOSALS OR PRIOR AGREEMENTS, ORAL, OR WRITTEN, AND ANY OTHER COMMUNICATIONS BETWEEN YOU AND THE COMPANY OR ANY REPRESENTATIVE OF THE COMPANY RELATING TO THE SUBJECT MATTER OF THIS AGREEMENT. If you are a U.S. Government user, this Software is licensed with "restricted rights" as set forth in subparagraphs (a)-(d) of the Commercial Computer-Restricted Rights clause at FAR 52.227-19 or in subparagraphs (c)(1)(ii) of the Rights in Technical Data and Computer Software clause at DFARS 252.227-7013, and similar clauses, as applicable.

Should you have any questions concerning this agreement or if you wish to contact the Company for any reason, please contact in writing: New Media / Higher Education Division / Prentice Hall Inc. / 1 Lake Street / Upper Saddle River, NJ 07458.